Alex Latimer

The Trouble with Earth

Andersen Press

For Isla and Lily

First published
in Great Britain in 2022 by
Andersen Press Ltd., 20 Vauxhall
Bridge Road, London SW1V 2SA, UK.
Vijverlaan 48, 3062 HL Rotterdam,
Nederland. Copyright © Alex Latimer 2022. The
right of Alex Latimer to be identified as the author
and illustrator of this work has been asserted by him
in accordance with

1   3   5   7   9   10   8   6   4   2

the Copyright, Designs and Patents Act, 1988.
Printed and bound in China. All rights
reserved. British Library Cataloguing
in Publication Data available.
ISBN 978 1 83913 081 6

Every year the planets take
A well-deserved midsummer break,
To read and swim and tan all day
Out somewhere in the Milky Way.

Now at last the day had come
To stop their orbit round the sun.
And so the planets waved goodbye
To their homes up in the sky.

They met on time at eight o'clock
On the corner of their block,
Then stood and waited in a line.
(The bus arrived at eight-oh-nine.)

"Jupiter, Venus, Mars – that's me –
Uranus? Check! And Mercury.

Neptune's here, and Saturn too.
Step right up and go on through.

Now, is there anyone I've missed?"
"Me!" said Earth. "Please check your list."

Mars checked: "Nope. Your name's not here.
But I can write it in... next year."

And then the planets closed the door.
"There's no space," they said, "for any more."
"Hang on!" called Earth. "Don't go! Just wait!
I'm sure there's room in there for eight!"

When Earth got home she stroked her moon
(Who was glad to have her back so soon).

"My friends were
really mean,"
she sighed.

And then she sat alone, and cried.

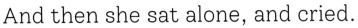

At last Earth stopped to wipe her face.
"Maybe… there really was no space?"

"No!" Earth knew something wasn't right
So she packed her car and drove all night.

She headed west and drove for hours
Through asteroids and meteor showers
And there beyond the brightest star,
Earth made a space to park her car.

She found eight planets in the tub!
(Pluto had since joined the club.)

She heard them laugh,
she heard them whoop
She saw Saturn with
her hula hoop.

Earth's eyes were wet, her heart was sore,
"Why don't you like me any more?"

"We're sorry, Earth.
Forgive us, please.
But it looks to us like
you have **fleas**!

We're worried
what you have
is catching!

We know you itch.
We've seen you
scratching!"

Earth stood still as it sank in,
Then slowly she began to grin.
"Fleas?!" She laughed until she shook.
"Come close," she said, "and take a look!"

The planets shrugged and gathered near
To peer into Earth's atmosphere.

And they saw...

... dolphins and
enormous whales
And fish with wings
(and fish with sails)

Flocks of birds
high in the air
And bugs that
flitted everywhere.

And below the bugs and below the birds
Were wildebeest in endless herds.
Grasses, flowers,
redwood trees!

And jungles full of chimpanzees.

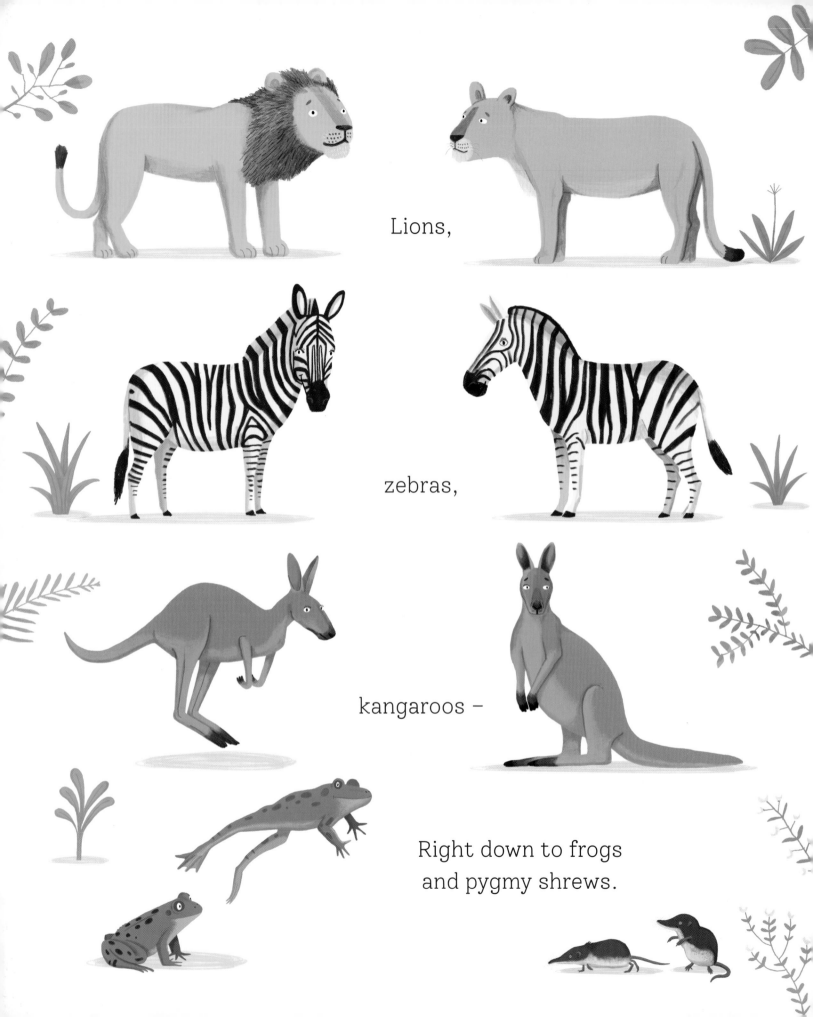

Lions,

zebras,

kangaroos –

Right down to frogs
and pygmy shrews.

Then smaller still –
the ants and
bees,

And yes,
down there,
they saw
some fleas.

hi!

"It's true," said Earth. "I am infested
Just as Mars here has suggested.
And it's not just fleas, there's so much more!
From mountain top to ocean floor!
I LOVE each creature, plant and bug
Each human, tree and tiny slug.

But don't be worried – don't be stressed –
Let me put your minds at rest:

You can't catch the things I've got.

You're too cold,

and you're too hot.

You're too small,

your days are long,

JUPITER your gravity is much too strong.

You're made of gas,

SATURN

you're made of ice,

URANUS

and Mars: you just
aren't very nice.

MARS

You have to be just right, you see.
And that is why there's life on me."

"Now we're jealous!" said the planets.
"We want fish and buck and gannets!
We want grasses! We want trees!
We'd love to have some chimpanzees!"

"You can't have those, I'm sad to say
But you can visit night or day.
I have biscuits, cakes and teas
Do come round and see my fleas.

And I will tell you
all about…
The life cycle of the
rainbow trout,
And what a warthog
likes the best,
And where to find
a weaver's nest.

And if you really want to know
Things that happened long ago –
The story of the giant sloth
And what might eat a poison moth!
And when to spot a giant squid,
And what those silly monkeys did,
And how a porcupine gives birth...
Oh, how I love my life!" said Earth.

The next year, for their summer break
They didn't make the same mistake.
"Earth," said Mars, "I must insist
That you are first upon my list."

They all drove west for many hours,
Past comets, stars and meteor showers
To read and swim and tan all day
Out somewhere in the Milky Way.